GW00391705

♥ ..I love you Mum ! ♥

You're the no.1 Mum in the world!

Juicylucy

ЯR
RAVETTE PUBLISHING

First published in 2008 by
Ravette Publishing Ltd
Unit 3, Tristar Centre, Star Road
Partridge Green, West Sussex RH13 8RA

www.juicylucydesigns.com

ISBN: 978-1-84161-300-0

..here's a little angel to remind you...

..of how much I love you...

three cheers for our
Magic Mummy!

hip, hip hooray!

You make such a difference in the world..

..Thank you!..

i love you more than...

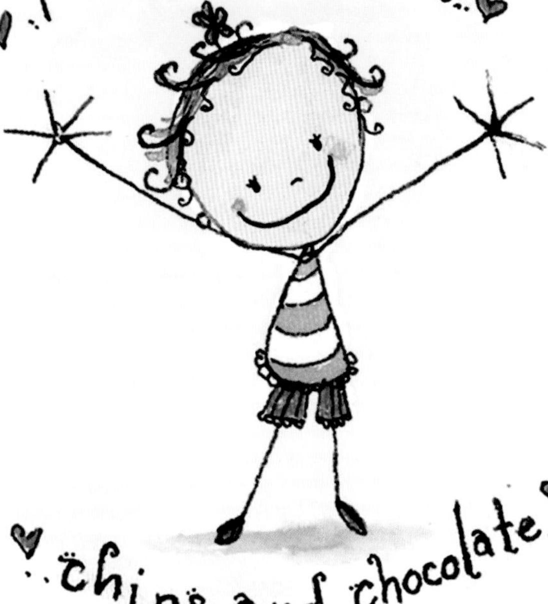

chips and chocolate.

a little magic
wish for you

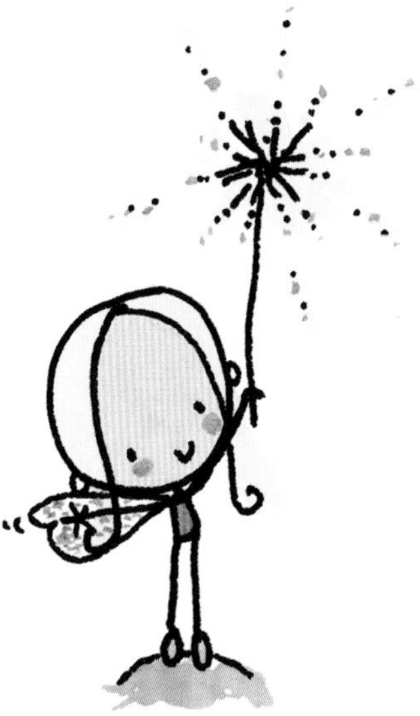

♥ ..I love you Mum ! ♥

I have been all around the universe and it is official
You are the Best mum EVER!

My beautiful Mummy !

..thankyou for giving me wings..♥

..all the little angels love you..

..and so do I ♥..

.. You're the best thing since
sliced bread..

Super-Mum

Thank-you for everything
you do..
You are Amazing!!

Mummy, I love you !

* You are the best
most beautiful *
most cuddliest
Mummy in all

of the whole
wide world. x

Have a really special

..Mother's Day! ..

*For a beautiful yummy Mummy!

You smell

♥ really

nice.

I'm so proud that you're my Mum. x

the
little
fairies
think
you
are rather
Special!

You're an angel!

thank you for your love, laughter
and inspiration!

Mummy..
I think you should put this crown on and never take it off..
for you are the Queen of mothers x

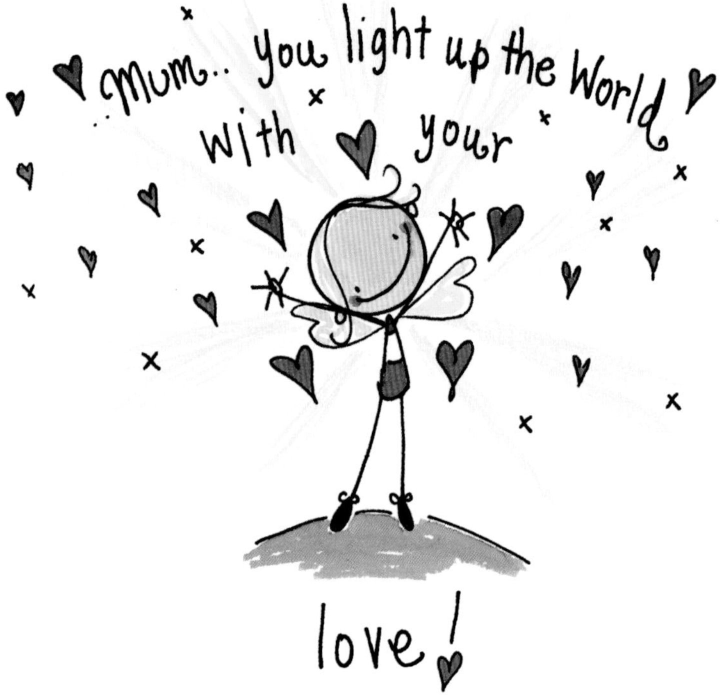
..Mum.. You light up the World
with your
love!

You're my mum,
my mate

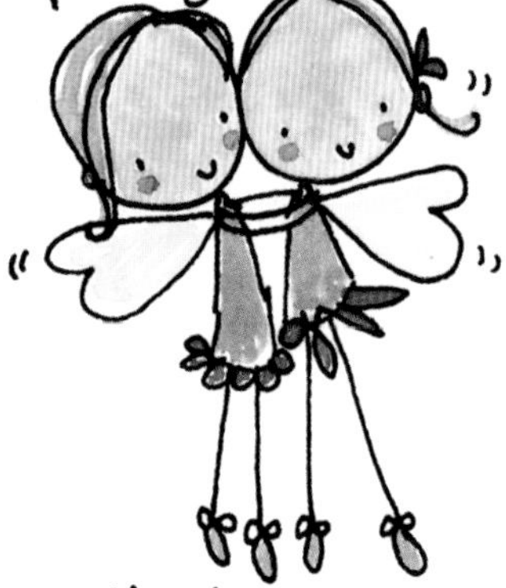

and I love
you x

♥ Mum! you are a magical angel!

...Thank you for all of your love!

*Officially the Best mum in the whole wide World!

You are special

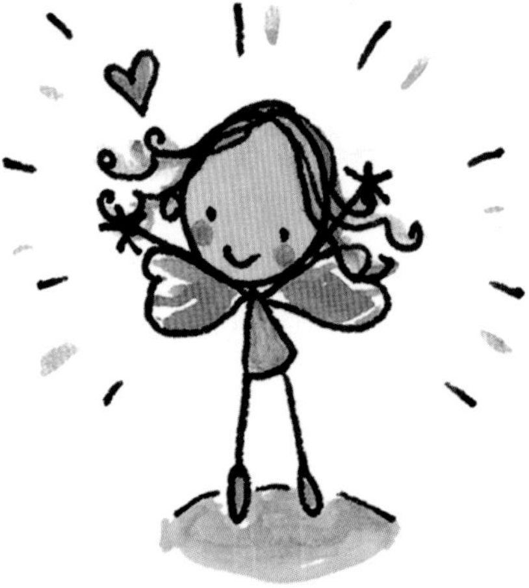

You're my mum and my mate,
let's drink tea, and...

...eat cake!

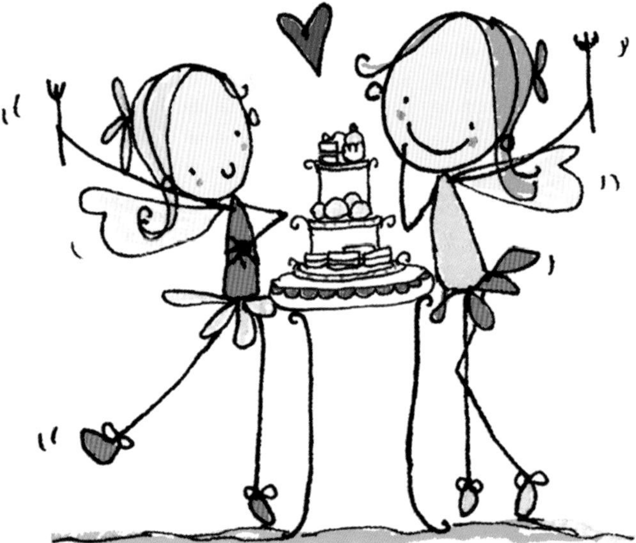

Mummy! I love you more than..

daddy.

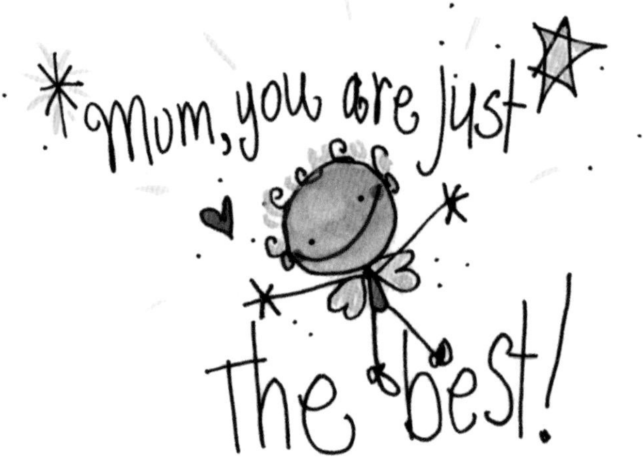
Mum, you are just
the best!

The little fairies think that you are
beautiful and special and kind!
They are thrilled that you have this book,
and want you to know that the lovely
people at Ravette have also published ...

	ISBN	Price
I love you	978-1-84161-298-0	£4.99
Let's be rudie nudies	978-1-84161-299-7	£4.99

HOW TO ORDER   Please send a cheque/postal order in £ sterling, made payable to 'Ravette Publishing' for the cover price of the books and allow the following for post & packaging ...

UK & BFPO   70p for the first book & 40p per book thereafter
Europe & Eire   £1.30 for the first book & 70p per book thereafter
Rest of the world   £2.20 for the first book & £1.10 per book thereafter

RAVETTE PUBLISHING LTD
Unit 3 Tristar Centre, Star Road, Partridge Green, West Sussex RH13 8RA
Tel: 01403 711443   Fax: 01403 711554   Email: ravettepub@aol.com
Prices and availability are subject to change without prior notice.